Know Your Scales!

The essential learning method for scales and arpeggio

GW01044903

Trumpet Grades 1, 2 & 3

Paul Harris

Contents

© 1997 by Faber Music Ltd
First published in 1997 by Faber Music Ltd
Bloomsbury House
74–77 Great Russell Street
London WC1B 3DA
Music and text typeset by Wessex Music Services
Cover design by S & M Tucker
Printed in England by Caligraving Ltd

ISBN10: 0-571-51728-5
EAN13: 978-0-571-51728-2

To buy Faber Music publications or to find out about the full range of titles available
please contact your local retailer or Faber Music sales enquiries:

Faber Music Limited, Burnt Mill, Elizabeth Way, Harlow, CM20 2HX England
Tel: +44 (0) 1279 82 89 82   Fax: +44 (0) 1279 82 89 83
sales@fabermusic.com   fabermusicstore.com

Introduction

To the student

Have you ever realised that it is much easier to learn something if you *want* to? Do you ever forget your telephone number? How many characters can you name from your favourite 'soap' or football team? Scales are not difficult to learn if you really *want* to learn them. Treat scales as friends – they will pay you great dividends.

To the teacher

Scales and arpeggios are often a real stumbling block for exam candidates and budding musicians. **Know Your Scales!** is designed to make scale preparation and learning fun – a scale book without scales!

Working through the book will encourage your pupils to approach scales and arpeggios methodically and thoughtfully. It will help with memory problems and turn scale learning into an enjoyable experience.

Knowing scales has many benefits – it helps improve technique, helps students to learn pieces more quickly (difficult passages in pieces are often nothing more than scale patterns), it will help in developing more fluent sight-reading and, of course, will help students to earn better marks in grade examinations.

Using the book

The purpose of this workbook is to incorporate regular scale playing into lessons and daily practice, and to help students prepare for grade examinations. New scales are introduced throughout the book, broadly in line with the grade 1, 2 and 3 requirements of the major examination boards, and each is divided into six sections. You need not work at all sections nor in the order as set out, but the best results may well be achieved by adhering fairly closely to the material.

Know the notes! is to prove that the actual notes *are* known! Students should be encouraged to say the notes up and down until this can be done *really* fluently.

The **Finger Fitness** exercises are to strengthen the fingers and to cover technically tricky areas. They should be played legato, detached and staccato. When they are fluent you may like to add dynamic levels and alter the rhythms and articulation patterns.

The **Scale Study** and **Arpeggio Study** place the material in context. Some have *ad lib.* accompaniments either for one or two extra players; use these whenever possible as they will add to the general enjoyment of performance during lessons and also help with rhythm and intonation.

Have a go is to encourage thought 'in the key', through the improvisation or composition of a short tune.

Say → think → play! is where the student finally plays the scale and arpeggio. The following method should really help the student memorise each scale and arpeggio:

1   **Say** the notes out loud, up and down, and repeat until fluent.

2   Say the notes out loud and finger the scale. Don't proceed further until this can be done confidently and accurately.

3   **Think** the notes and finger the scale (but don't play).

4   Think the notes and **play**. By this time there should be no doubt in your mind and there should certainly be no fumbles or wrong notes!

Marking

A marking system has been included to help you and the student monitor progress and to act as a means of encouragement. It is suggested you adopt a grading system as follows:

A   Excellent work!

B   Good work, but keep at it!

C   A little more practice would be a good idea!

D   No time to lose – get practising at once!

Revision

At the end of each stage you will find a **Revision Practice** table. As the new scales become more familiar you will wish your student to revise them regularly. This table is to encourage a methodical approach to scale practice, and show that there are endless ways of practising scales and arpeggios! Fill out the table for each week, or each practice session as follows:

1   Mark **L** for legato, **D** for detached and **S** for staccato, or

2   choose a different articulation pattern each time from the following:

Scales:

Arpeggios:

3   Choose a different rhythmic pattern each time from the following:

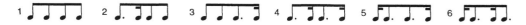

4   Finally, choose a different dynamic level. As students get into the habit of good scale and arpeggio practice they should no longer need the table.

Group teaching

Know Your Scales! is ideal for group teaching. Members of the group should be asked to comment on performances of the **Finger Fitness** exercises – was the tone even? Were the fingers moving rhythmically and together when necessary? Was the pulse even? *etc.* Exercises could be split between two or more players (e.g. playing alternate phrases), and constructive criticism should be encouraged for the scale and arpeggio studies. With the optional *ad lib.* parts, a small group of the pieces could be performed at a private 'group concert', or even at a more formal concert.

The author would like to thank Debbie Arscott and Mark Holt for many helpful suggestions.

C major 1 octave

Know the Notes!

1 Write the key signature of C major:

2 Write out the notes of the scale:

3 Write out the notes of the arpeggio:

Finger Fitness

Always practise the **Finger Fitness** exercises legato, detached and staccato (see Introduction).

Cranberry Crumble

Scale study in C major

Cavalry Charge!   Arpeggio study in C major

Have a go

Compose or improvise your own tune in C major. If you are writing your tune down, remember to put in some markings and then give your piece a title.

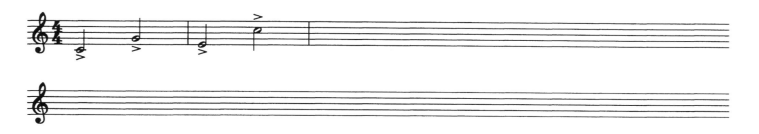

Say
Think
Play!

Say the notes out loud, up and down, then say the notes out loud and finger the scale/arpeggio.

Think the notes and finger the scale/arpeggio.

Play the scale and arpeggio.

Revision Practice

C major (1 octave)	1	2	3	4	5	6	7	8	9	10
Legato/Detached/Staccato										
Articulation pattern										
Rhythmic pattern										
Dynamic level										

Marking

C major (1 octave)	Grade
Know the notes!	
Finger fitness	
Scale study	
Arpeggio study	
Have a go	
Say → think → play!	

A minor 1 octave

Know the Notes!

1 Write the key signature of A minor:

2 Write out the notes of the harmonic scale:

3 Write out the notes of the melodic scale:

up →

←down

4 Write out the notes of the arpeggio:

Finger Fitness

Arabian Apricot   Scale study in A harmonic minor

Acorn Aria

Scale study in A melodic minor

Anchors Away!

Arpeggio study in A minor

Have a go

Compose or improvise your own tune using the notes of A harmonic minor.

Have another go
Compose or improvise your own tune using the notes of A melodic minor.

Say
Think
Play!

Say the notes out loud, up and down, then say the notes out loud and finger the scale/arpeggio.

Think the notes and finger the scale/arpeggio.

Play the scale and arpeggio.

Revision Practice

A minor (1 octave)	1	2	3	4	5	6	7	8	9	10
Harmonic/Melodic										
Legato/Detached/Staccato										
Articulation pattern										
Rhythmic pattern										
Dynamic level										

Marking

A minor (1 octave)	Grade
Know the notes!	
Finger fitness	
Scale study (harmonic)	
Scale study (melodic)	
Arpeggio study	
Have a go	
Have another go	
Say → think → play!	

D major 1 octave

Know the Notes!

1 Write the key signature of D major:

2 Write out the notes of the scale:

3 Write out the notes of the arpeggio:

Finger Fitness

Dainty Damsel   Scale study in D major

Dragon Drama   Arpeggio study in D major

Have a go   Compose or improvise your own tune in D major.

Say

Think

Play!

Say the notes out loud, up and down, then say the notes out loud and finger the scale/arpeggio.

Think the notes and finger the scale/arpeggio.

Play the scale and arpeggio.

Revision Practice

D major (1 octave)	1	2	3	4	5	6	7	8	9	10
Legato/Detached/Staccato										
Articulation pattern										
Rhythmic pattern										
Dynamic level										

Marking

D major (1 octave)	Grade
Know the notes!	
Finger fitness	
Scale study	
Arpeggio study	
Have a go	
Say → think → play!	

B♭ major 1 octave

Know the Notes!

1 Write the key signature of B♭ major:

2 Write out the notes of the scale:

3 Write out the notes of the arpeggio:

Finger Fitness

Banana Boat

Scale study in B♭ major

Brief Bagatelle   Arpeggio study in B♭ major

Have a go   Compose or improvise your own tune in B♭ major.

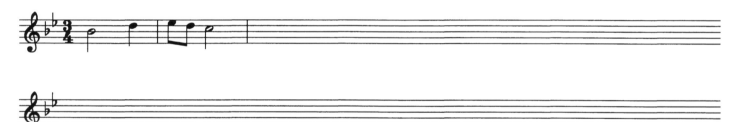

Say
Think
Play!

Say the notes out loud, up and down, then say the notes out loud and finger the scale/arpeggio.

Think the notes and finger the scale/arpeggio.

Play the scale and arpeggio.

Revision Practice

B♭ major (1 octave)	1	2	3	4	5	6	7	8	9	10
Legato/Detached/Staccato										
Articulation pattern										
Rhythmic pattern										
Dynamic level										

Marking

B♭ major (1 octave)	Grade
Know the notes!	
Finger fitness	
Scale study	
Arpeggio study	
Have a go	
Say → think → play!	

D minor 1 octave

Know the Notes!

1 Write the key signature of D minor:

2 Write out the notes of the harmonic scale:

3 Write out the notes of the melodic scale:

up →

←down

4 Write out the notes of the arpeggio:

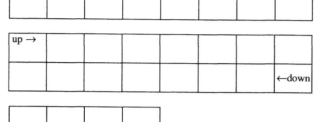

Finger Fitness

Dotty Ditty

Scale study in D harmonic minor

Devilish!   Scale study in D melodic minor

Ding-dong Drone   Arpeggio study in D minor

Have a go   Compose or improvise your own tune using the notes of D harmonic minor.

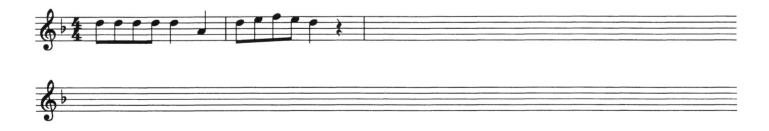

Have another go

Compose or improvise your own tune using the notes of D melodic minor.

Say
Think
Play!

Say the notes out loud, up and down, then say the notes out loud and finger the scale/arpeggio.

Think the notes and finger the scale/arpeggio.

Play the scale and arpeggio.

Revision Practice

D minor (1 octave)	1	2	3	4	5	6	7	8	9	10
Harmonic/Melodic										
Legato/Detached/Staccato										
Articulation pattern										
Rhythmic pattern										
Dynamic level										

Marking

D minor (1 octave)	Grade
Know the notes!	
Finger fitness	
Scale study (harmonic)	
Scale study (melodic)	
Arpeggio study	
Have a go	
Have another go	
Say → think → play!	

E major 1 octave

Know the Notes!

1 Write the key signature of E major:

2 Write out the notes of the scale:

3 Write out the notes of the arpeggio:

Finger Fitness

Eloping Elephants   Scale study in E major

'E'zee Exercise   Arpeggio study in E major

Have a go   Compose or improvise your own tune in E major.

Say
Think
Play!

Say the notes out loud, up and down, then say the notes out loud and finger the scale/arpeggio.

Think the notes and finger the scale/arpeggio.

Play the scale and arpeggio.

Revision Practice

E major (1 octave)	1	2	3	4	5	6	7	8	9	10
Legato/Detached/Staccato										
Articulation pattern										
Rhythmic pattern										
Dynamic level										

Marking

E major (1 octave)	Grade
Know the notes!	
Finger fitness	
Scale study	
Arpeggio study	
Have a go	
Say → think → play!	

F major 1 octave

Know the Notes!

1 Write the key signature of F major:

2 Write out the notes of the scale:

3 Write out the notes of the arpeggio:

Finger Fitness

Fruity

Scale study in F major

Festive Fanfare   Arpeggio study in F major

Have a go   Compose or improvise your own tune in F major.

Say

Think

Play!

Say the notes out loud, up and down, then say the notes out loud and finger the scale/arpeggio.

Think the notes and finger the scale/arpeggio.

Play the scale and arpeggio.

Revision Practice

F major (1 octave)	1	2	3	4	5	6	7	8	9	10
Legato/Detached/Staccato										
Articulation pattern										
Rhythmic pattern										
Dynamic level										

Marking

F major (1 octave)	Grade
Know the notes!	
Finger fitness	
Scale study	
Arpeggio study	
Have a go	
Say → think → play!	

E♭ major 1 octave

Know the Notes!

1 Write the key signature of E♭ major:

2 Write out the notes of the scale:

3 Write out the notes of the arpeggio:

Finger Fitness

Ebbtide

Scale study in E♭ major

Excitable Elf

Arpeggio study in E♭ major

Have a go

Compose or improvise your own tune in E♭ major.

Say

Think

Play!

Say the notes out loud, up and down, then say the notes out loud and finger the scale/arpeggio.

Think the notes and finger the scale/arpeggio.

Play the scale and arpeggio.

Revision Practice

E♭ major (1 octave)	1	2	3	4	5	6	7	8	9	10
Legato/Detached/Staccato										
Articulation pattern										
Rhythmic pattern										
Dynamic level										

Marking

E♭ major (1 octave)	Grade
Know the notes!	
Finger fitness	
Scale study	
Arpeggio study	
Have a go	
Say → think → play!	

A major 12th

Know the Notes!

1 Write the key signature of A major:

2 Write out the notes of the scale:

3 Write out the notes of the arpeggio:

Finger Fitness

Aubade

Scale study in A major

Andante espressivo

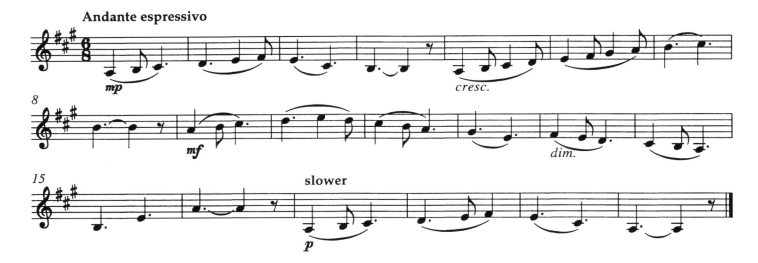

Arietta

Arpeggio study in A major

Player 2
(ad lib.)

Have a go

Compose or improvise your own tune in A major.

Say

Think

Play!

Say the notes out loud, up and down, then say the notes out loud and finger the scale/arpeggio.

Think the notes and finger the scale/arpeggio.

Play the scale and arpeggio.

Revision Practice

A major (12th)	1	2	3	4	5	6	7	8	9	10
Legato/Detached/Staccato										
Articulation pattern										
Rhythmic pattern										
Dynamic level										

Marking

A major (12th)	Grade
Know the notes!	
Finger fitness	
Scale study	
Arpeggio study	
Have a go	
Say → think → play!	

E minor 1 octave

Know the Notes!

1 Write the key signature of E minor:

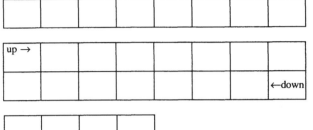

2 Write out the notes of the harmonic scale:

3 Write out the notes of the melodic scale:

up →

←down

4 Write out the notes of the arpeggio:

Finger Fitness

Eastern Elegy

Scale study in E harmonic minor

Easter Egg

Scale study in E melodic minor

Exams are Extremely Enjoyable

Arpeggio study in E minor

Have a go

Compose or improvise your own tune using the notes of E harmonic minor.

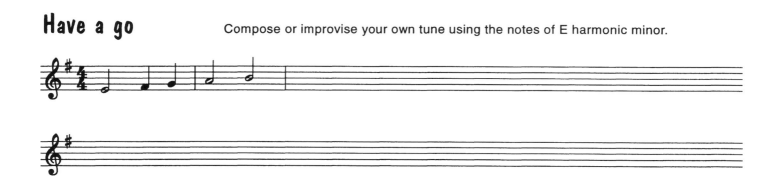

Have another go

Compose or improvise your own tune using the notes of E melodic minor.

Say
Think
Play!

Say the notes out loud, up and down, then say the notes out loud and finger the scale/arpeggio.

Think the notes and finger the scale/arpeggio.

Play the scale and arpeggio.

Revision Practice

E minor (1 octave)	1	2	3	4	5	6	7	8	9	10
Harmonic/Melodic										
Legato/Detached/Staccato										
Articulation pattern										
Rhythmic pattern										
Dynamic level										

Marking

E minor (1 octave)	Grade
Know the notes!	
Finger fitness	
Scale study (harmonic)	
Scale study (melodic)	
Arpeggio study	
Have a go	
Have another go	
Say → think → play!	

C minor 1 octave

Know the Notes!

1 Write the key signature of C minor:

2 Write out the notes of the harmonic scale:

3 Write out the notes of the melodic scale:

up →

←down

4 Write out the notes of the arpeggio:

Finger Fitness

Carriage Clock

Scale study in C harmonic minor

Moderato - like the ticking of a clock

Chariots

Scale study in C melodic minor

Con fuoco

Caramel Caprice

Arpeggio study in C minor

Allegretto

Have a go

Compose or improvise your own tune using the notes of C harmonic minor.

Have another go

Compose or improvise your own tune using the notes of C melodic minor.

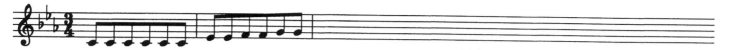

Say
Think
Play!

Say the notes out loud, up and down, then say the notes out loud and finger the scale/arpeggio.

Think the notes and finger the scale/arpeggio.

Play the scale and arpeggio.

Revision Practice

C minor (1 octave)	1	2	3	4	5	6	7	8	9	10
Harmonic/Melodic										
Legato/Detached/Staccato										
Articulation pattern										
Rhythmic pattern										
Dynamic level										

Marking

C minor (1 octave)	Grade
Know the notes!	
Finger fitness	
Scale study (harmonic)	
Scale study (melodic)	
Arpeggio study	
Have a go	
Have another go	
Say → think → play!	

Performance tips

1   Always play scales and arpeggios with your best tone quality.

2   Tone quality must be as even as possible throughout.

3   Don't land on the last note with a 'bump'.

4   Make sure the tips of your fingers are placed on the tops of the valves - always avoid flat fingers.

5   Rhythm must be even, and pulse steady throughout.

6   Make sure all notes are of equal duration in tongued scales and arpeggios.

7   Don't change tempo or lose rhythmic control when you change direction.

8   Don't accent the top note.

9   Always play scales carefully in tune.

10   Make sure that your finger movement is well co-ordinated in arpeggios.

11   At exams, play all scales at the same tempo and about *mezzo-forte (mf)*.

12   Remember that scales *are* music; play each one with shape and direction.

Scales and Arpeggios

E minor (1 octave)
harmonic

melodic

C minor (1 octave)
harmonic

melodic

Chromatic scale

Beginning on C (1 octave)